On the First Day of Kindergarten

To my grandsons, Cole and Chase, with love — T.R.

For Little Eddie — L.H.

ISBN 978-1-338-19376-3

12 11 10 9 8 7 6 5 4 3   17 18 19 20 21 22

Printed in the U.S.A.   40

First Scholastic printing, May 2017

The artist used ink, paint, and collage to create the digital illustrations for this book.
Typography by Chelsea C. Donaldson

On the First Day

# of Kindergarten

by Tish Rabe pictures by Laura Hughes

SCHOLASTIC INC.

On the first day of kindergarten

I thought it was so cool

riding the bus to my school!

On the second day of kindergarten

I thought it was so cool

making lots of friends

and riding the bus to my school!

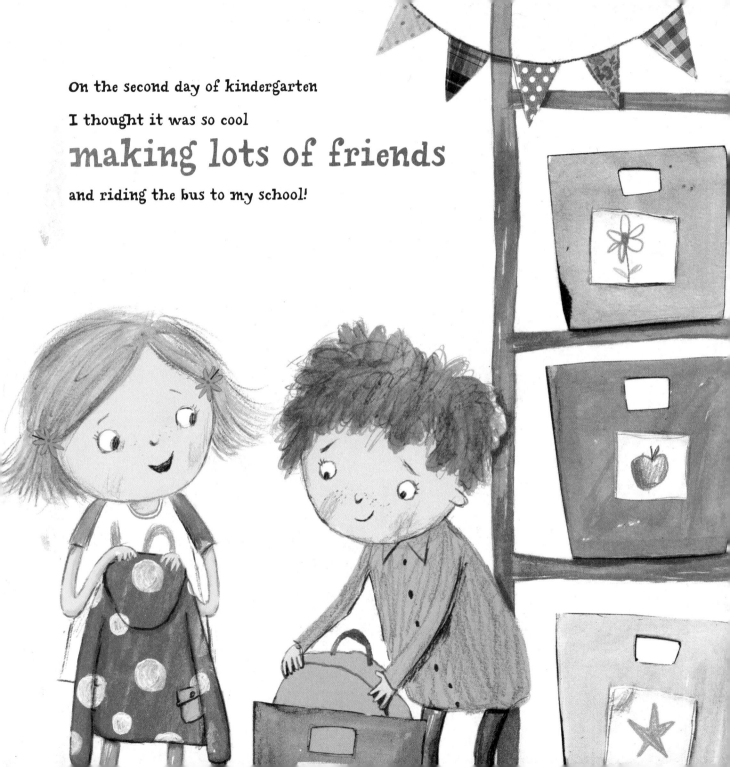

On the third day of kindergarten
I thought it was so cool

counting up to ten,

making lots of friends,

and riding the bus to my school!

On the fourth day of kindergarten
I thought it was so cool

running in a race,

counting up to ten,

making lots of friends,

and riding the bus to my school!

On the fifth day of kindergarten
I thought it was so cool

SINGING A SONG!

running in a race,
counting up to ten,
making lots of friends,
and riding the bus to my school!

On the sixth day of kindergarten
I thought it was so cool

sliding down the slide,

SINGING A SONG!
running in a race,
counting up to ten,
making lots of friends,
and riding the bus to my school!

On the seventh day of kindergarten

I thought it was so cool

sorting by shapes,

sliding down the slide,
SINGING A SONG!
running in a race,
counting up to ten,
making lots of friends,
and riding the bus to my school!

On the eighth day of kindergarten
I thought it was so cool
sharing a story,

sorting by shapes,
sliding down the slide,
SINGING A SONG!
running in a race,
counting up to ten,
making lots of friends,
and riding the bus to my school!

On the ninth day of kindergarten
I thought it was so cool
painting a picture,

sharing a story,
sorting by shapes,
sliding down the slide,
SINGING A SONG!
running in a race,
counting up to ten,
making lots of friends,
and riding the bus to my school!

On the tenth day of kindergarten
I thought it was so cool

laughing at lunch,

painting a picture,
sharing a story,
sorting by shapes,
sliding down the slide,
SINGING A SONG!
running in a race,
counting up to ten,
making lots of friends,
and riding the bus to my school!

On the eleventh day of kindergarten

I thought it was so cool

jumping rope in gym,

laughing at lunch,

painting a picture,

sharing a story,

sorting by shapes,

sliding down the slide,

SINGING A SONG!

running in a race,

counting up to ten,

making lots of friends,

and riding the bus to my school!

On the twelfth day of kindergarten

I thought it was so cool

going on a field trip,

jumping rope in gym,
laughing at lunch,
painting a picture,
sharing a story,
sorting by shapes,
sliding down the slide,
SINGING A SONG!

running in a race,
counting up to ten,
making lots of friends,

AND RIDING THE BUS TO MY SCHOOL!

WE LOVE SCHOOL!